RAGS

Progressive piano solos

ARRANGED BY STEPHEN DURO

Chester Music
(A division of Music Sales Limited)
8/9 Frith Street
London W1V 5TZ

PREFACE

Here are 15 pieces carefully selected from the repertoire of ragtime piano compositions. The golden age of ragtime lasted from approximately 1896 to 1917 and the pieces which appear in this album all date from this period. Ragtime piano music is usually characterised by a syncopated melody in the right hand against which the left hand provides a steady rhythmical background. It would be a mistake to suppose, however, that all ragtime compositions are intended to create the same atmosphere. Many are intended to be vibrant, joyous pieces; but there are also a number which evoke quite different nostalgic and poetic emotions.

As is the case with all instrumental music, a performance will only come to life in the hands of a pianist who has invested the time and effort to master not only the technical requirements (which in the case of some of the pieces is considerable) but also the subtleties of dynamics, phrasing and articulation inherent in the music.

These pieces are arranged according to difficulty, with the easier pieces (approximately Grade II to III standard of the Associated Board) appearing first, and the harder ones (Grade V/VI standard) towards the end. Fingering, where indicated, is intended as a guide only and should be altered to suit the needs of individual players.

Stephen Duro

Visit the Music Sales Internet Music Shop
at http://www.musicsales.co.uk

This book © Copyright 1997 Chester Music
Order No. CH61282 ISBN 0-7119-6440-8

Music processed by Allegro Reproductions.
Cover design by 4i Limited.
Printed in the United Kingdom by Caligraving Limited, Thetford, Norfolk.

CONTENTS

FLY, YOU BLACKBIRDS

From Brainard's Ragtime Collection (1899)

The syncopated melodic line against a regular left hand pattern is a feature of ragtime. Slow practice of bars 1 to 4 will help you to develop this style of playing.

WEEPING WILLOW

By Scott Joplin

Notice the unexpected modulation to the B dominant seventh chord in bar 13, a reminder that Scott Joplin was a 'poet' among ragtime composers. For maximum effect, try playing this piece in a gentle style.

THE ENTERTAINER

By Scott Joplin

A feature of this piece is the subtle use of dynamics, for example the *crescendo* in bar 6. Make sure your rendition does justice to the various dynamic markings.

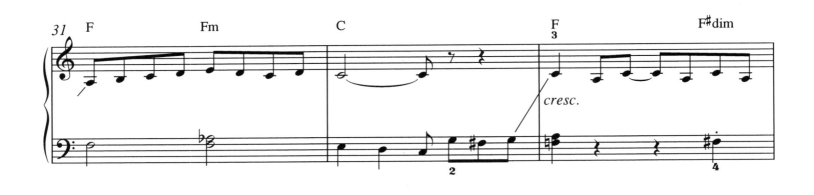

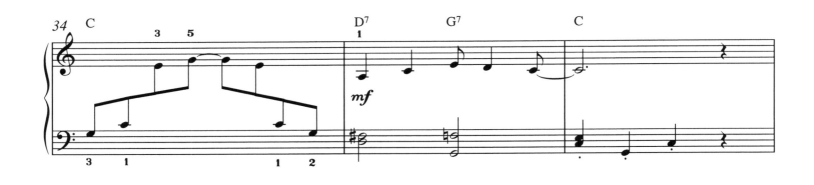

HELLO, MA BABY

Words & music by Joseph E. Howard & Ida Emerson

Notice how the melodic line is characterised by a semibreve in bars 4, 6 and 8. This provides an opportunity to bring out the figure, beginning on the second beat, in the left hand.

THE BOS'N RAG

By Fred S. Stone

A jaunty style suits this piece. Notice how the second section begins quietly and gradually builds. Many ragtime pieces, such as this, benefit from careful attention to dynamic markings.

LIVING A RAGTIME LIFE

Words & music by Gene Jefferson & Robert Roberts
Arranged & adapted by Max Morath

The left hand keeps this piece moving along.
Note that the crotchet notes in the bass should
be played in a light, *staccato* way throughout.

COTTON BOLLS

By Charles Hunter

This is a fine example of an extended ragtime composition. To obtain the best effect in performance you should carefully observe all dynamic markings.

FINE

15

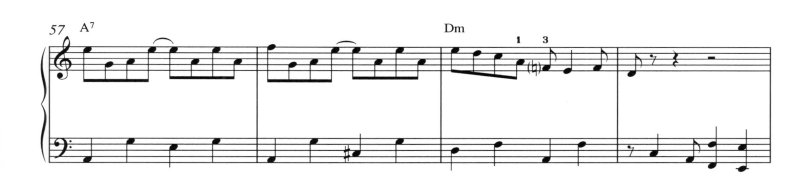

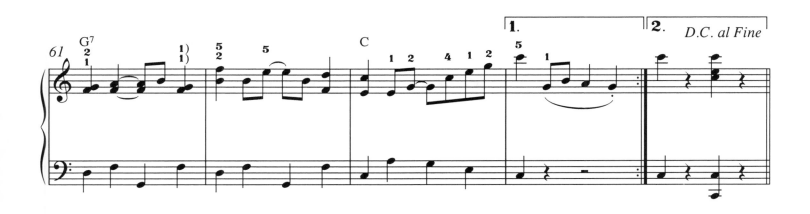

MANDY'S BROADWAY STROLL

By Thomas E. Broady

This piece will sound best taken at a pleasant walking tempo, in other words not too fast. Try putting a slight accent on the first note of the phrase beginning at bar 5 and in similar places.

CLASSICAL RAG

By E. J. Stark

Whilst virtuosic writing is to be found in abundance among the ragtime composers, poetry can also be found. This piece makes its effect not by outward display but by careful use of dynamics and use of contrasted sections.

PEACHES AND CREAM

By Percy Wenrich

A brief review of your scales will assist you in this piece. Notice how the right hand passage work in bars 15 and 18 are based on the C major scale, whereas 22 and 23 are based on the scale of A minor.

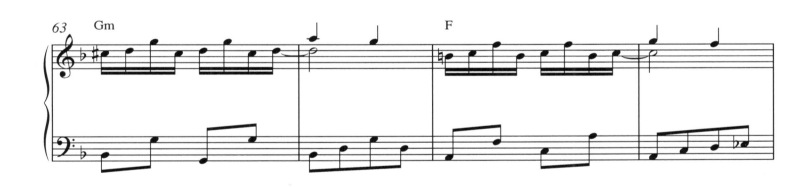

THE ST. LOUIS RAG

By Tom Turpin

A successful performance of this piece requires agility and rhythmic control. For example, the semiquaver run at bar 24, repeated at bar 32, needs to be practised slowly several times.

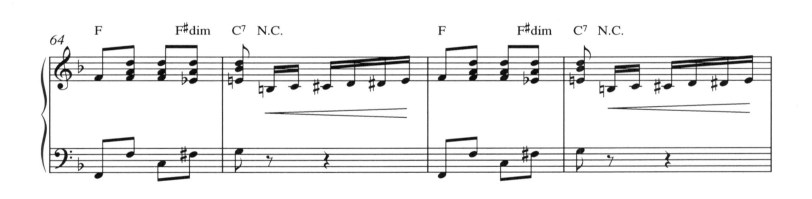

CALICO RAG

By Lee B. Grabbe

You need to maintain a sense of flow in a piece of this type, especially at bar 38 which seems to signal the end. For this reason, do not slow up and avoid giving too big an accent to the second chord in the bar.

MAPLE LEAF RAG

By Scott Joplin

This is one of the most famous pieces associated with ragtime. In order to bring out all of its subtleties, it is best played at not too fast a tempo and with careful attention to dynamic marks and phrasing.

BLACK AND WHITE RAG

By George Botsford

This popular piece has considerable melodic and rhythmic vitality. It is also a useful study for developing finger dexterity. You will need to practise some passages, e.g. bars 22 and 23, slowly at first in order to gain fluency.

THE SYCAMORE

By Scott Joplin

A jaunty tempo suits this piece. It makes demands upon the performer and the octave passages beginning at bar 22 require some slow practice in order to obtain fluency.

Moderately bright

Also in this series...

The complete series of progressive piano solos, graded from Associated Board grades III to V. Each piece is arranged and fingered in authentic style and includes helpful playing and style notes, fingering and chord symbols.

JUST BLUES
Basin Street Blues, Angel Eyes,
The Lady Sings The Blues
...and many more.
CH61056

JUST JAZZ
Caravan, Fascinating Rhythm,
Lullaby of Birdland
...and many more.
CH61057

JUST LATIN
The Girl From Ipanema,
One Note Samba, Desafinado
...and many more.
CH61217

JUST ROCK
Wonderwall, All Shook Up,
Can't Buy Me Love
...and many more.
CH61218

JUST POP
Unchained Melody, Fernando,
Every Breath You Take, Hey Jude
...and many more.
CH61280

JUST SWING
Honeysuckle Rose,
Sophisticated Lady, Come Fly With Me
...and many more.
CH61281

JUST RAGS
The Entertainer, Maple Leaf Rag,
Black And White Rag
...and many more.
CH61282

Also in this series:
JUST JAZZ for alto saxophone and piano accompaniment
JUST BLUES for alto saxophone and piano accompaniment

Chester Music Limited
Exclusive distributors:
Music Sales Limited, Newmarket Road,
Bury St Edmunds, Suffolk IP33 3YB.